THE FOLD IN FUN

COLORING BOOK

by Sharon Jones

PRICE/STERN/SLOAN

Publishers, Inc., Los Angeles

1983

ISBN: 0-8431-1026-0

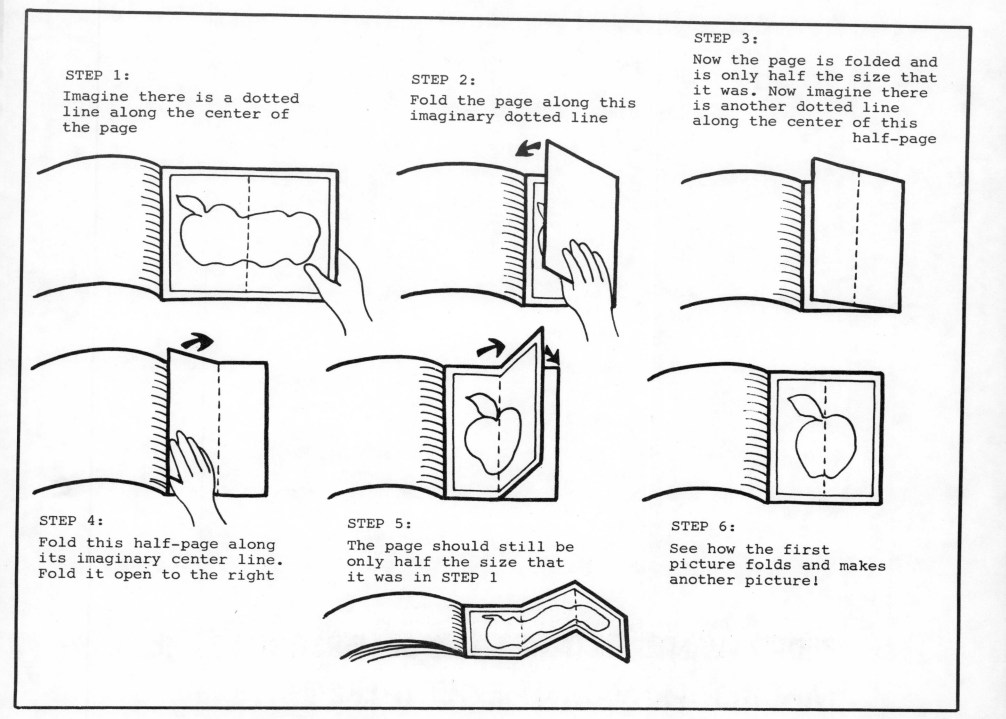

STEP 1:

Imagine there is a dotted line along the center of the page

STEP 2:

Fold the page along this imaginary dotted line

STEP 3:

Now the page is folded and is only half the size that it was. Now imagine there is another dotted line along the center of this half-page

STEP 4:

Fold this half-page along its imaginary center line. Fold it open to the right

STEP 5:

The page should still be only half the size that it was in STEP 1

STEP 6:

See how the first picture folds and makes another picture!

PEDRO WANTS TO TAKE HIS SOMBREROS TO THE
MARKET. HOW CAN HE GET THERE ?

A

B

A

B

THiS MAN iS iN THE PARK.
WHAT iS HE SELLING ?

AT NIGHT, YOU CAN SEE FIREFLIES.
WHAT BIRD COMES OUT AT NIGHT?

JOEY IS SAD. HIS BIRTHDAY CAKE IS MISSING SOMETHING. WHAT IS IT?

A

B

HAPPY BIRTHDAY

HAPPY BIRTHDAY

A

B

THE GLASS SLIPPER DOES NOT FIT THE UGLY STEPSISTERS.
CAN YOU HELP THE PRINCE FIND CINDERELLA ?

THE PRINCESS HAS BEEN LOCKED IN THE ROYAL DUNGEON
BY THE WICKED WITCH. CAN YOU HELP HER ESCAPE?

ROYAL DUNGEON

IN HAWAii THEY GROW COCONUTS.
WHAT OTHER FRUIT COMES FROM HAWAii?

A B

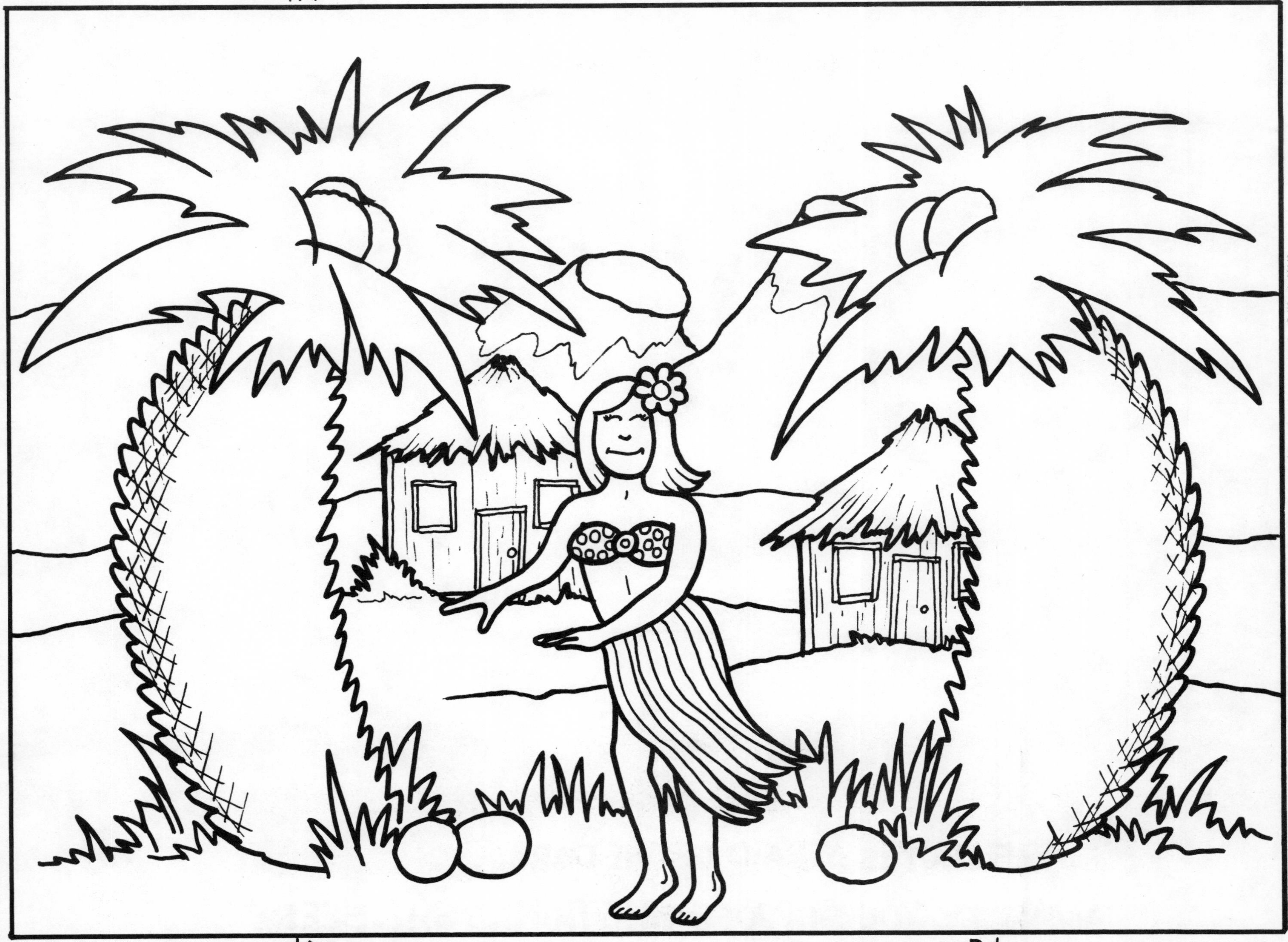

A B

LITTLE LUCY is AFRAID OF THE DARK.

WHAT DO YOU SUPPOSE SHE THINKS SHE SEES?

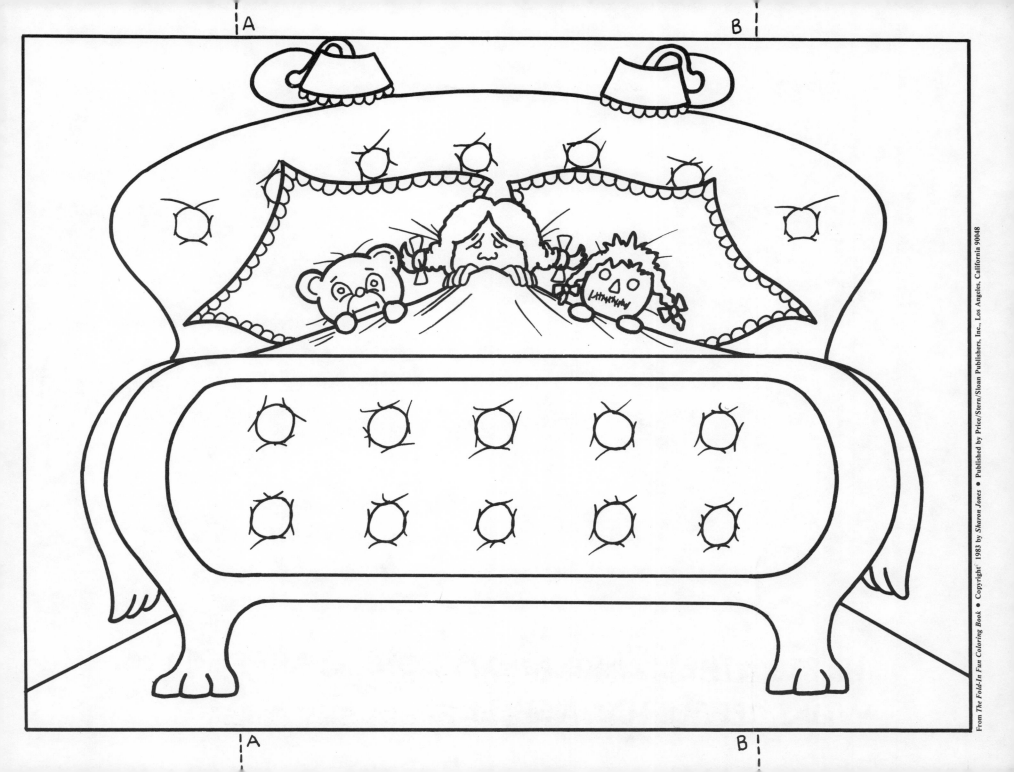

THE FROG, THE LIZARD AND THE SNAKE ARE REPTILES.
WHAT REPTILE HAS A SHELL?

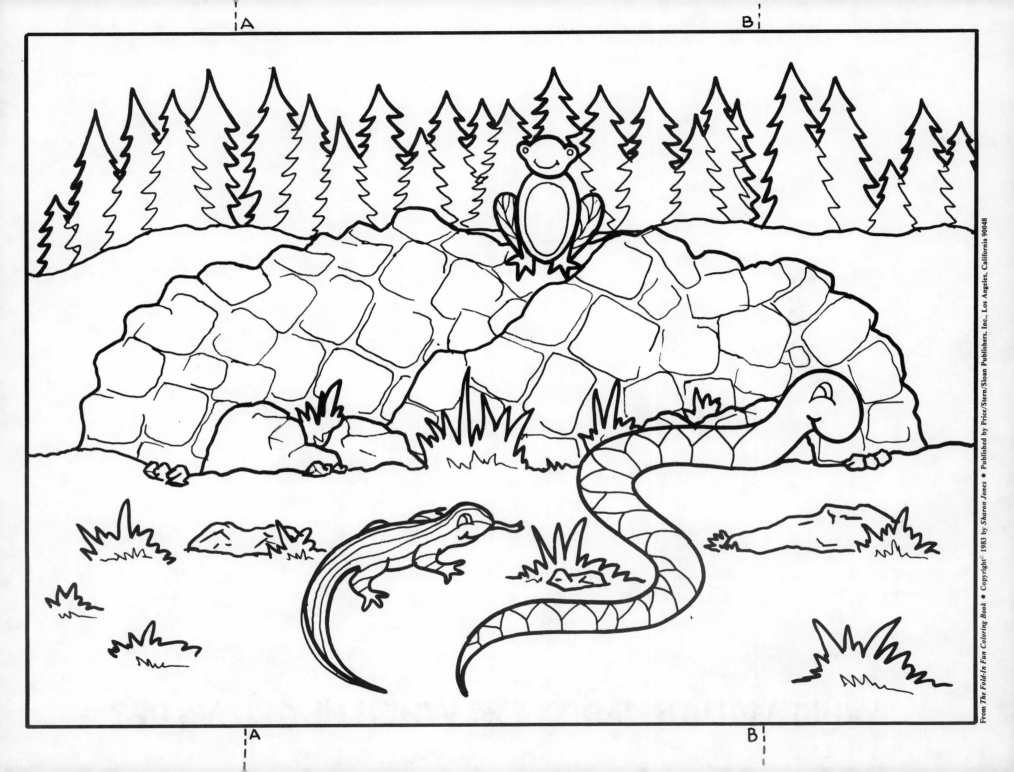

WHAT WILL THE TADPOLE BE WHEN HE GROWS UP?

SID THE SNAKE WANTS TO KNOW WHAT LETTER
COMES AFTER R IN THE ALPHABET. CAN YOU HELP HIM?

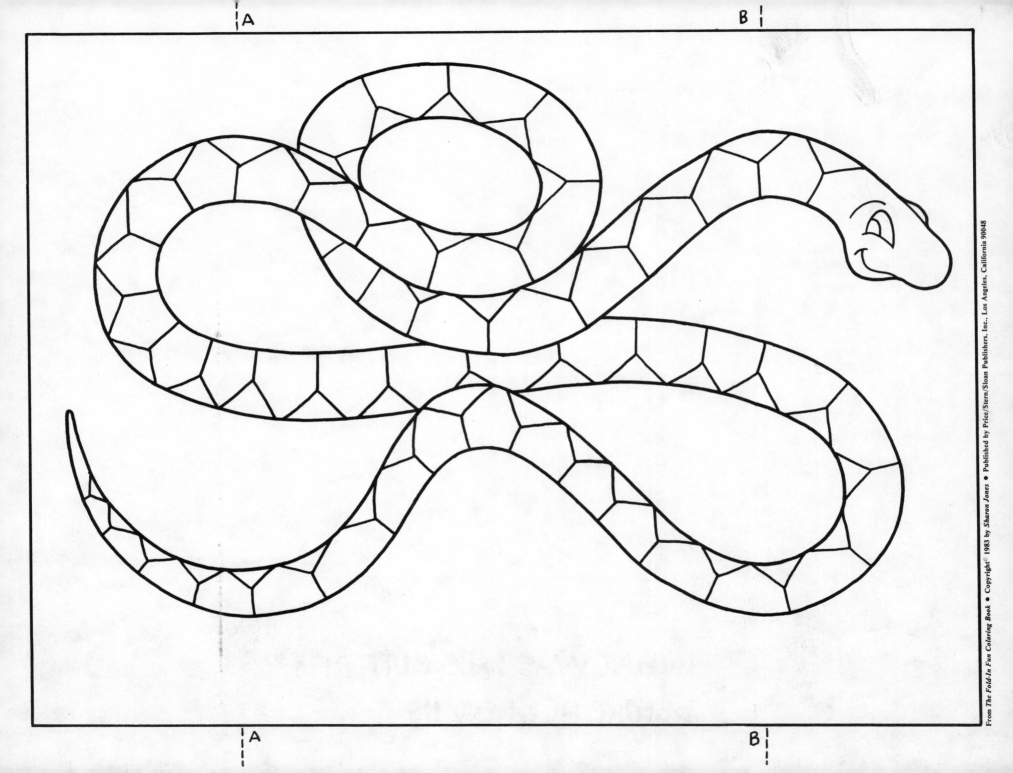

A

B

A

B

WHAT WAS THiS BUTTERFLY
BEFORE HE GREW UP ?

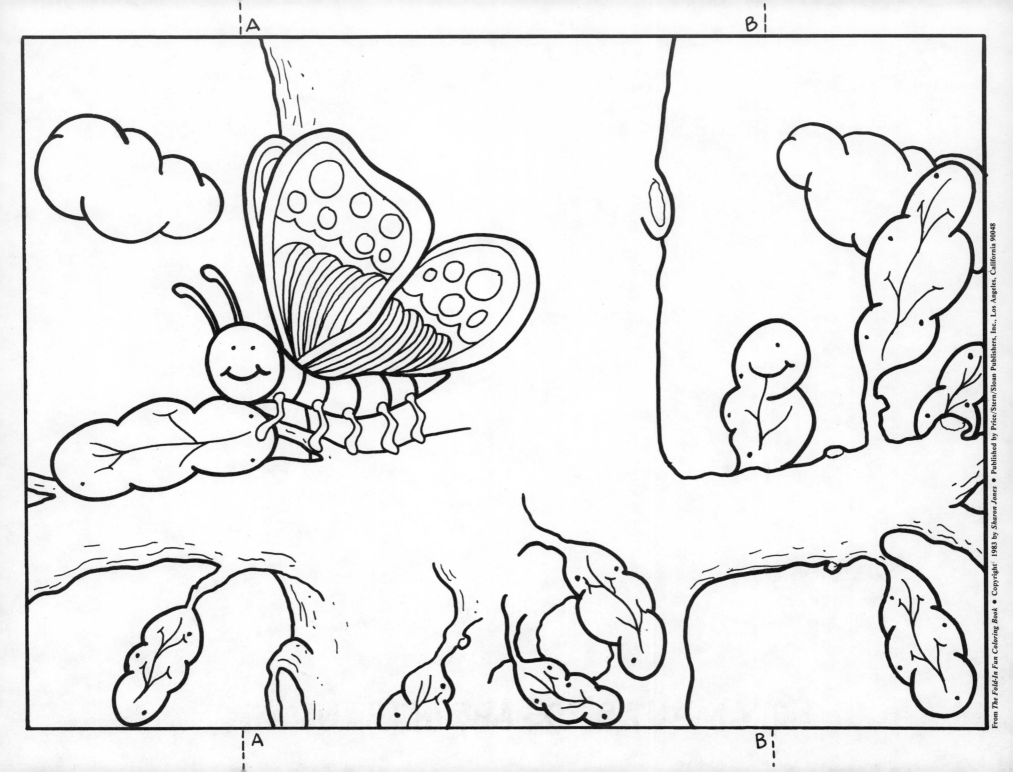

HOW MANY BiRDS ARE iN THE NEST ?

A

B

A

B

THE BABY KANGAROO HAS GOTTEN HIMSELF INTO
SOME TROUBLE. CAN YOU HELP HIM GET BACK TO HIS MOTHER?

FRANK'S WAGON HAS LOST ITS WHEEL. HE HAS FOUND
A SCREW TO HELP HIM PUT IT BACK ON, BUT HE
DOESN'T KNOW WHAT TOOL TO USE. CAN YOU FIND
THE RIGHT ONE?

WE ALL SHOULD GO TO THE DENTIST REGULARLY, BUT MEANWHILE, WHAT DO WE NEED TO DO TO KEEP OUR TEETH HEALTHY?

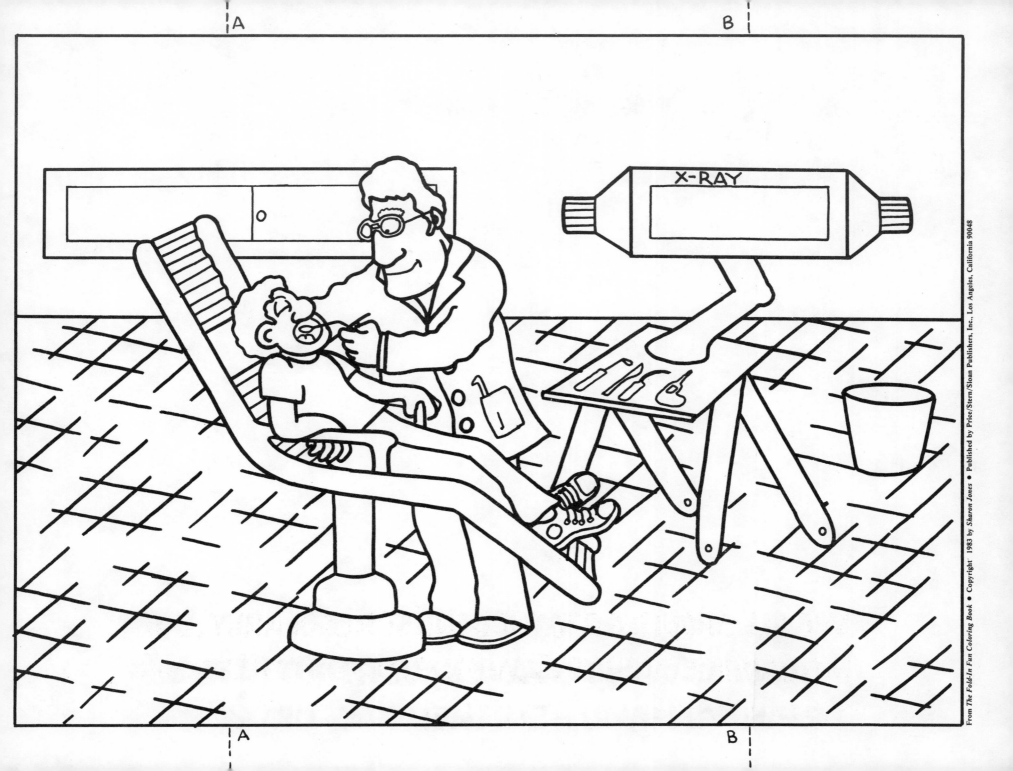

TIMMY AND HIS DOG ARE CAUGHT OUT IN THE RAIN. CAN YOU HELP THEM STAY DRY?

BiLLY WANTS TO BE AN ASTRONAUT SOMEDAY.
CAN YOU HELP HiM MAKE HiS DREAM COME TRUE?

HERE ARE SOME OF THE THINGS A COWBOY WEARS.
WHAT IS ONE IMPORTANT THING THAT IS MISSING?

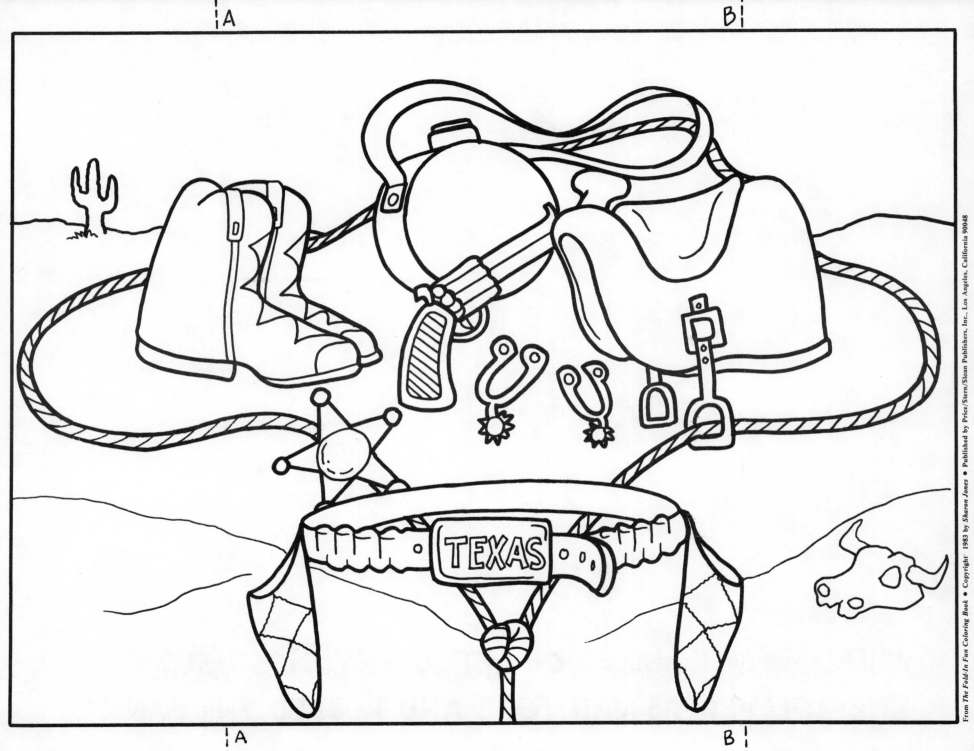

WHERE DID JACK AND AL GO AFTER THEY DISGUISED
THEMSELVES AS JANITORS AND ROBBED THE BANK?

MILDRED THE MAID HAS TO CLEAN SYLVESTER'S
ROOM. WHAT WOULD MAKE HER JOB EASIER ?

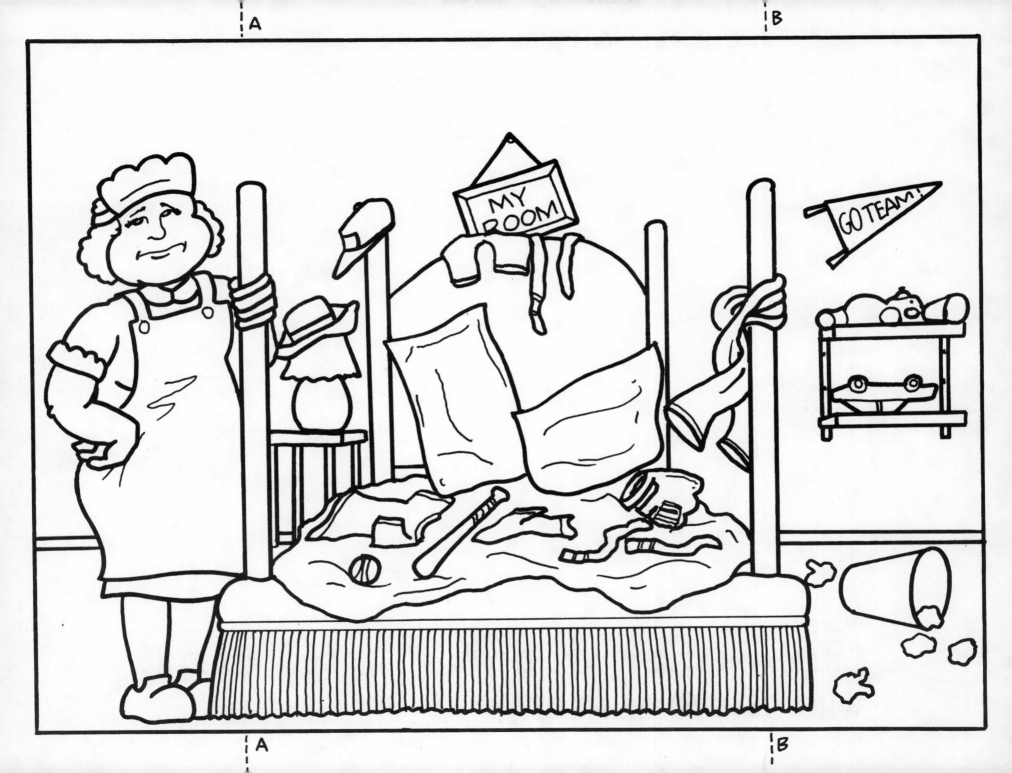

BILLY AND SUSIE ARE GIVING THE DOG A BATH.
WHO GETS TO BE NEXT?

*Price/Stern/Sloan also publishes such other
unique and highly creative coloring books as:*

THE DESIGNS TO COLOR SERIES
(available in six completely different versions)

TANKS AND ARMORED VEHICLES
COLORING BOOK

FROM DISTANT GALAXIES COLORING BOOK

ANIMAL DESIGNS COLORING BOOK
NO. 1 and NO. 2

MASKS TO COLOR, CUT OUT AND WEAR!

MORE MASKS TO COLOR, CUT OUT AND WEAR!

THE MAGICAL WORLD COLORING BOOK

THE STAINED GLASS COLORING BOOK
NO.1, NO. 2 and NO. 3

STAR CRUISERS COLORING BOOK
NO. 1 and NO. 2

THE ROBOT COLORING BOOK

OFF-ROAD VEHICLES COLORING BOOK

THE BUTTERFLY COLORING BOOK

and many, many more

They available in book, stationery and toy stores or
may be ordered directly from the publisher. For a
complete list of titles send a *stamped,
self-addressed envelope* to:

PRICE/STERN/SLOAN   *Publishers, Inc.*
410 North La Cienega Boulevard, Los Angeles, California 90048